I have a new baseball mitt and one of my lucky sneakers.

Mom, where is my other lucky sneaker?

Is it in my toy chest?

Is it under my bed?

Is it in my closet?

Is it in my little sister's bubble bath?

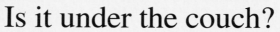

Is it under the couch?

Is it in the cabinet?

Is it in the box?

Mom, that's not my lucky sneaker.
These are new sneakers!

Is it in the garbage can?

That's okay, Mom. I'll just save my new sneakers for the next game.